This
Goal Planner
2021
Belongs To

_____

_____

D1578405

Calendar 2021

January

Mon	Tue	Wed	Thu	Fri	Sat	Sun
				1	2	3
4	5	6	7	8	9	10
11	12	13	14	15	16	17
18	19	20	21	22	23	24
25	26	27	28	29	30	31

February

Mon	Tue	Wed	Thu	Fri	Sat	Sun
1	2	3	4	5	6	7
8	9	10	11	12	13	14
15	16	17	18	19	20	21
22	23	24	25	26	27	28

March

Mon	Tue	Wed	Thu	Fri	Sat	Sun
1	2	3	4	5	6	7
8	9	10	11	12	13	14
15	16	17	18	19	20	21
22	23	24	25	26	27	28
29	30	31				

April

Mon	Tue	Wed	Thu	Fri	Sat	Sun
			1	2	3	4
5	6	7	8	9	10	11
12	13	14	15	16	17	18
19	20	21	22	23	24	25
26	27	28	29	30		

May

Mon	Tue	Wed	Thu	Fri	Sat	Sun
31					1	2
3	4	5	6	7	8	9
10	11	12	13	14	15	16
17	18	19	20	21	22	23
24	25	26	27	28	29	30

June

Mon	Tue	Wed	Thu	Fri	Sat	Sun
	1	2	3	4	5	6
7	8	9	10	11	12	13
14	15	16	17	18	19	20
21	22	23	24	25	26	27
28	29	30				

Calendar 2021

July

Mon	Tue	Wed	Thu	Fri	Sat	Sun
			1	2	3	4
5	6	7	8	9	10	11
12	13	14	15	16	17	18
19	20	21	22	23	24	25
26	27	28	29	30	31	

August

Mon	Tue	Wed	Thu	Fri	Sat	Sun
30	31					1
2	3	4	5	6	7	8
9	10	11	12	13	14	15
16	17	18	19	20	21	22
23	24	25	26	27	28	29

September

Mon	Tue	Wed	Thu	Fri	Sat	Sun
		1	2	3	4	5
6	7	8	9	10	11	12
13	14	15	16	17	18	19
20	21	22	23	24	25	26
27	28	29	30			

October

Mon	Tue	Wed	Thu	Fri	Sat	Sun
				1	2	3
4	5	6	7	8	9	10
11	12	13	14	15	16	17
18	19	20	21	22	23	24
25	26	27	28	29	30	31

November

Mon	Tue	Wed	Thu	Fri	Sat	Sun
1	2	3	4	5	6	7
8	9	10	11	12	13	14
15	16	17	18	19	20	21
22	23	24	25	26	27	28
29	30					

December

Mon	Tue	Wed	Thu	Fri	Sat	Sun
		1	2	3	4	5
6	7	8	9	10	11	12
13	14	15	16	17	18	19
20	21	22	23	24	25	26
27	28	29	30	31		

2021 Resolution

Physical Health	Mental Health

Social	Soul/Spirit

2021 Resolution

Family	Finance

Career	Other

Monthly Resolution

January	February
March	**April**
May	**June**

Monthly Resolution

July	August

September	October

November	December

January

Mon	Tue	Wed	Thu	Fri	Sat	Sun
				1	2	3
4	5	6	7	8	9	10
11	12	13	14	15	16	17
18	19	20	21	22	23	24
25	26	27	28	29	30	31

February

Mon	Tue	Wed	Thu	Fri	Sat	Sun
1	2	3	4	5	6	7
8	9	10	11	12	13	14
15	16	17	18	19	20	21
22	23	24	25	26	27	28

March

Mon	Tue	Wed	Thu	Fri	Sat	Sun
1	2	3	4	5	6	7
8	9	10	11	12	13	14
15	16	17	18	19	20	21
22	23	24	25	26	27	28
29	30	31				

April

Mon	Tue	Wed	Thu	Fri	Sat	Sun
			1	2	3	4
5	6	7	8	9	10	11
12	13	14	15	16	17	18
19	20	21	22	23	24	25
26	27	28	29	30		

May

Mon	Tue	Wed	Thu	Fri	Sat	Sun
31					1	2
3	4	5	6	7	8	9
10	11	12	13	14	15	16
17	18	19	20	21	22	23
24	25	26	27	28	29	30

June

Mon	Tue	Wed	Thu	Fri	Sat	Sun
	1	2	3	4	5	6
7	8	9	10	11	12	13
14	15	16	17	18	19	20
21	22	23	24	25	26	27
28	29	30				

July

Mon	Tue	Wed	Thu	Fri	Sat	Sun
			1	2	3	4
5	6	7	8	9	10	11
12	13	14	15	16	17	18
19	20	21	22	23	24	25
26	27	28	29	30	31	

August

Mon	Tue	Wed	Thu	Fri	Sat	Sun
30	31					1
2	3	4	5	6	7	8
9	10	11	12	13	14	15
16	17	18	19	20	21	22
23	24	25	26	27	28	29

September

Mon	Tue	Wed	Thu	Fri	Sat	Sun
		1	2	3	4	5
6	7	8	9	10	11	12
13	14	15	16	17	18	19
20	21	22	23	24	25	26
27	28	29	30			

October

Mon	Tue	Wed	Thu	Fri	Sat	Sun
				1	2	3
4	5	6	7	8	9	10
11	12	13	14	15	16	17
18	19	20	21	22	23	24
25	26	27	28	29	30	31

November

Mon	Tue	Wed	Thu	Fri	Sat	Sun
1	2	3	4	5	6	7
8	9	10	11	12	13	14
15	16	17	18	19	20	21
22	23	24	25	26	27	28
29	30					

December

Mon	Tue	Wed	Thu	Fri	Sat	Sun
		1	2	3	4	5
6	7	8	9	10	11	12
13	14	15	16	17	18	19
20	21	22	23	24	25	26
27	28	29	30	31		

Goal Planner

| ○ Physical Health | ○ Mental Health | ○ Soul/Spirit | ○ Social |
| ○ Family | ○ Finance | ○ Career | ○ Other |

Goal

Start Date	Due Date

What do I want to achieve?

_____
_____
_____
_____
_____

How will I achieve my goal?

_____
_____
_____
_____
_____

What means the most to me?

_____
_____
_____
_____

Focus on...

_____
_____
_____
_____

Action Plan

Date	Action Steps

Goal Planner

◯ Physical Health	◯ Mental Health	◯ Soul/Spirit	◯ Social
◯ Family	◯ Finance	◯ Career	◯ Other

Goal

Start Date	Due Date

What I want to achieve?

How I will achieve my goal?

What means most to me?

Focus on...

Action Plan

Date	Action Steps

Goal Planner

| ○ | Physical Health | ○ | Mental Health | ○ | Soul/Spirit | ○ | Social |
| ○ | Family | ○ | Finance | ○ | Career | ○ | Other |

Goal

	Start Date	Due Date	

What do I want to achieve?

How will I achieve my goal?

What means the most to me?

Focus on...

Action Plan

Date	Action Steps

Goal Planner

○ Physical Health	○ Mental Health	○ Soul/Spirit	○ Social
○ Family	○ Finance	○ Career	○ Other

Goal

Start Date	Due Date

What I want to achieve?

How I will achieve my goal?

What means most to me?

Focus on...

Action Plan

Date	Action Steps

Goal Planner

○ Physical Health	○ Mental Health	○ Soul/Spirit	○ Social
○ Family	○ Finance	○ Career	○ Other

Goal

Start Date	Due Date

What do I want to achieve?

How will I achieve my goal?

What means the most to me?

Focus on...

Action Plan

Date	Action Steps

Goal Planner

○	Physical Health	○	Mental Health	○	Soul/Spirit	○	Social
○	Family	○	Finance	○	Career	○	Other

Goal

	Start Date	Due Date	

What I want to achieve?

How I will achieve my goal?

What means most to me?

Focus on...

Action Plan

Date	Action Steps

Goal Planner

○ Physical Health	○ Mental Health	○ Soul/Spirit	○ Social
○ Family	○ Finance	○ Career	○ Other

Goal

Start Date	Due Date

What do I want to achieve?

How will I achieve my goal?

What means the most to me?

Focus on...

Action Plan

Date	Action Steps

Goal Planner

- ( ) Physical Health
- ( ) Mental Health
- ( ) Soul/Spirit
- ( ) Social
- ( ) Family
- ( ) Finance
- ( ) Career
- ( ) Other

Goal

Start Date	Due Date

What I want to achieve?

How I will achieve my goal?

What means most to me?

Focus on...

Action Plan

Date	Action Steps

Goal Planner

○ Physical Health	○ Mental Health	○ Soul/Spirit	○ Social
○ Family	○ Finance	○ Career	○ Other

Goal

Start Date	Due Date

What do I want to achieve?

How will I achieve my goal?

What means the most to me?

Focus on...

Action Plan

Date	Action Steps

Goal Planner

○ Physical Health	○ Mental Health	○ Soul/Spirit	○ Social
○ Family	○ Finance	○ Career	○ Other

Goal

Start Date	Due Date

What I want to achieve?

How I will achieve my goal?

What means most to me?

Focus on...

Action Plan

Date	Action Steps

Goal Planner

○ Physical Health	○ Mental Health	○ Soul/Spirit	○ Social
○ Family	○ Finance	○ Career	○ Other

Goal

	Start Date	Due Date	

What do I want to achieve?

How will I achieve my goal?

What means the most to me?

Focus on...

Action Plan

Date	Action Steps

Goal Planner

○ Physical Health	○ Mental Health	○ Soul/Spirit	○ Social
○ Family	○ Finance	○ Career	○ Other

Goal

	Start Date	Due Date	

What I want to achieve?

How I will achieve my goal?

What means most to me?

Focus on...

Action Plan

Date	Action Steps

Goal Planner

| ○ Physical Health | ○ Mental Health | ○ Soul/Spirit | ○ Socia |
| ○ Family | ○ Finance | ○ Career | ○ Other |

Goal

| | Start Date | Due Date | |
| | | | |

What do I want to achieve?

How will I achieve my goal?

What means the most to me?

Focus on...

Action Plan

Date	Action Steps

Goal Planner

○ Physical Health	○ Mental Health	○ Soul/Spirit	○ Social
○ Family	○ Finance	○ Career	○ Other

Goal

	Start Date	Due Date	

What I want to achieve?

How I will achieve my goal?

What means most to me?

Focus on...

Action Plan

Date	Action Steps

Goal Planner

- ◯ Physical Health
- ◯ Mental Health
- ◯ Soul/Spirit
- ◯ Socia
- ◯ Family
- ◯ Finance
- ◯ Career
- ◯ Other

Goal

Start Date	Due Date

What do I want to achieve?

How will I achieve my goal?

What means the most to me?

Focus on...

Action Plan

Date	Action Steps

Goal Planner

⚪ Physical Health	⚪ Mental Health	⚪ Soul/Spirit	⚪ Social
⚪ Family	⚪ Finance	⚪ Career	⚪ Other

Goal

Start Date	Due Date

What I want to achieve?

How I will achieve my goal?

What means most to me?

Focus on...

Action Plan

Date	Action Steps

Goal Planner

| ○ Physical Health | ○ Mental Health | ○ Soul/Spirit | ○ Socia |
| ○ Family | ○ Finance | ○ Career | ○ Othe |

Goal

Start Date	Due Date

What do I want to achieve?

How will I achieve my goal?

What means the most to me?

Focus on...

Action Plan

Date	Action Steps

Goal Planner

○ Physical Health	○ Mental Health	○ Soul/Spirit	○ Social
○ Family	○ Finance	○ Career	○ Other

Goal

	Start Date	Due Date	

What I want to achieve?

How I will achieve my goal?

What means most to me?

Focus on...

Action Plan

Date	Action Steps

Goal Planner

| ○ Physical Health | ○ Mental Health | ○ Soul/Spirit | ○ Socia |
| ○ Family | ○ Finance | ○ Career | ○ Other |

Goal

	Start Date	Due Date	

What do I want to achieve?	*How will I achieve my goal?*

What means the most to me?	*Focus on...*

Action Plan

Date	Action Steps

Goal Planner

○	Physical Health	○	Mental Health	○	Soul/Spirit	○	Social
○	Family	○	Finance	○	Career	○	Other

Goal

Start Date	Due Date

What I want to achieve?

How I will achieve my goal?

What means most to me?

Focus on...

Action Plan

Date	Action Steps

Goal Planner

○	Physical Health	○	Mental Health	○	Soul/Spirit	○ Social
○	Family	○	Finance	○	Career	○ Other

Goal

	Start Date	Due Date	

What do I want to achieve?

How will I achieve my goal?

What means the most to me?

Focus on...

Action Plan

Date	Action Steps

Goal Planner

○ Physical Health	○ Mental Health	○ Soul/Spirit	○ Social
○ Family	○ Finance	○ Career	○ Other

Goal

Start Date	Due Date

What I want to achieve?

How I will achieve my goal?

What means most to me?

Focus on...

Action Plan

Date	Action Steps

Goal Planner

○ Physical Health	○ Mental Health	○ Soul/Spirit	○ Socia
○ Family	○ Finance	○ Career	○ Othe

Goal

Start Date	Due Date

What do I want to achieve?

How will I achieve my goal?

What means the most to me?

Focus on...

Action Plan

Date	Action Steps

Goal Planner

○ Physical Health	○ Mental Health	○ Soul/Spirit	○ Social
○ Family	○ Finance	○ Career	○ Other

Goal

Start Date	Due Date

What I want to achieve?

How I will achieve my goal?

What means most to me?

Focus on...

Action Plan

Date	Action Steps

Goal Planner

○ Physical Health	○ Mental Health	○ Soul/Spirit	○ Social
○ Family	○ Finance	○ Career	○ Other

Goal

Start Date	Due Date

What do I want to achieve?

How will I achieve my goal?

What means the most to me?

Focus on...

Action Plan

Date	Action Steps

Goal Planner

○ Physical Health	○ Mental Health	○ Soul/Spirit	○ Social
○ Family	○ Finance	○ Career	○ Other

Goal

	Start Date	Due Date	

What I want to achieve?

How I will achieve my goal?

What means most to me?

Focus on...

Action Plan

Date	Action Steps

Goal Planner

○	Physical Health	○	Mental Health	○	Soul/Spirit	○	Social
○	Family	○	Finance	○	Career	○	Other

Goal

Start Date	Due Date

What do I want to achieve?

How will I achieve my goal?

What means the most to me?

Focus on...

Action Plan

Date	Action Steps

Goal Planner

○ Physical Health	○ Mental Health	○ Soul/Spirit	○ Social
○ Family	○ Finance	○ Career	○ Other

Goal

Start Date	Due Date

What I want to achieve?

How I will achieve my goal?

What means most to me?

Focus on...

Action Plan

Date	Action Steps

Goal Planner

○	Physical Health	○	Mental Health	○	Soul/Spirit	○	Social
○	Family	○	Finance	○	Career	○	Other

Goal

Start Date	Due Date

What do I want to achieve?

_____
_____
_____
_____
_____

How will I achieve my goal?

_____
_____
_____
_____
_____

What means the most to me?

_____
_____
_____
_____
_____

Focus on...

_____
_____
_____
_____
_____

Action Plan

Date	Action Steps

Goal Planner

○ Physical Health	○ Mental Health	○ Soul/Spirit	○ Social
○ Family	○ Finance	○ Career	○ Other

Goal

Start Date	Due Date

What I want to achieve?

How I will achieve my goal?

What means most to me?

Focus on...

Action Plan

Date	Action Steps

Goal Planner

| ○ | Physical Health | ○ | Mental Health | ○ | Soul/Spirit | ○ | Socia |
| ○ | Family | ○ | Finance | ○ | Career | ○ | Othe |

Goal

	Start Date	Due Date	

What do I want to achieve?

How will I achieve my goal?

What means the most to me?

Focus on...

Action Plan

Date	Action Steps

Goal Planner

○ Physical Health	○ Mental Health	○ Soul/Spirit	○ Social
○ Family	○ Finance	○ Career	○ Other

Goal

	Start Date	Due Date	

What I want to achieve?

How I will achieve my goal?

What means most to me?

Focus on...

Action Plan

Date	Action Steps

Goal Planner

○	Physical Health	○	Mental Health	○	Soul/Spirit	○	Social
○	Family	○	Finance	○	Career	○	Other

Goal

	Start Date	Due Date	

What do I want to achieve?

How will I achieve my goal?

What means the most to me?

Focus on...

Action Plan

Date	Action Steps

Goal Planner

○ Physical Health	○ Mental Health	○ Soul/Spirit	○ Social
○ Family	○ Finance	○ Career	○ Other

Goal

	Start Date	Due Date

What I want to achieve?

How I will achieve my goal?

What means most to me?

Focus on...

Action Plan

Date	Action Steps

Goal Planner

| ○ Physical Health | ○ Mental Health | ○ Soul/Spirit | ○ Socia |
| ○ Family | ○ Finance | ○ Career | ○ Othe |

Goal

	Start Date	Due Date	

What do I want to achieve?

How will I achieve my goal?

What means the most to me?

Focus on...

Action Plan

Date	Action Steps

Goal Planner

○ Physical Health	○ Mental Health	○ Soul/Spirit	○ Social
○ Family	○ Finance	○ Career	○ Other

Goal

Start Date	Due Date

What I want to achieve?

How I will achieve my goal?

What means most to me?

Focus on...

Action Plan

Date	Action Steps

Goal Planner

○ Physical Health	○ Mental Health	○ Soul/Spirit	○ Social
○ Family	○ Finance	○ Career	○ Other

Goal

Start Date	Due Date

What do I want to achieve?

How will I achieve my goal?

What means the most to me?

Focus on...

Action Plan

Date	Action Steps

Goal Planner

○ Physical Health	○ Mental Health	○ Soul/Spirit	○ Social
○ Family	○ Finance	○ Career	○ Other

Goal

	Start Date	Due Date	

What I want to achieve?

How I will achieve my goal?

What means most to me?

Focus on...

Action Plan

Date	Action Steps

Goal Planner

| ○ Physical Health | ○ Mental Health | ○ Soul/Spirit | ○ Socia |
| ○ Family | ○ Finance | ○ Career | ○ Othe |

Goal

Start Date	Due Date

What do I want to achieve?

_____
_____
_____
_____
_____

How will I achieve my goal?

_____
_____
_____
_____

What means the most to me?

_____
_____
_____
_____

Focus on...

_____
_____
_____

Action Plan

Date	Action Steps

Goal Planner

○ Physical Health	○ Mental Health	○ Soul/Spirit	○ Social
○ Family	○ Finance	○ Career	○ Other

Goal

	Start Date	Due Date	

What I want to achieve?

How I will achieve my goal?

What means most to me?

Focus on...

Action Plan

Date	Action Steps

Goal Planner

| ○ Physical Health | ○ Mental Health | ○ Soul/Spirit | ○ Socia |
| ○ Family | ○ Finance | ○ Career | ○ Othe |

Goal

| | Start Date | Due Date | |
| | | | |

What do I want to achieve?

How will I achieve my goal?

What means the most to me?

Focus on...

Action Plan

Date	Action Steps

Goal Planner

○ Physical Health	○ Mental Health	○ Soul/Spirit	○ Social
○ Family	○ Finance	○ Career	○ Other

Goal

Start Date	Due Date

What I want to achieve?

How I will achieve my goal?

What means most to me?

Focus on...

Action Plan

Date	Action Steps

Goal Planner

| ○ Physical Health | ○ Mental Health | ○ Soul/Spirit | ○ Socia |
| ○ Family | ○ Finance | ○ Career | ○ Other |

Goal

Start Date	Due Date

What do I want to achieve?

How will I achieve my goal?

What means the most to me?

Focus on...

Action Plan

Date	Action Steps

Goal Planner

○ Physical Health	○ Mental Health	○ Soul/Spirit	○ Social
○ Family	○ Finance	○ Career	○ Other

Goal

Start Date	Due Date

What I want to achieve?

How I will achieve my goal?

What means most to me?

Focus on...

Action Plan

Date	Action Steps

Goal Planner

| ○ Physical Health | ○ Mental Health | ○ Soul/Spirit | ○ Socia |
| ○ Family | ○ Finance | ○ Career | ○ Other |

Goal

	Start Date	Due Date	

What do I want to achieve?

How will I achieve my goal?

What means the most to me?

Focus on...

Action Plan

Date	Action Steps

Goal Planner

○ Physical Health	○ Mental Health	○ Soul/Spirit	○ Social
○ Family	○ Finance	○ Career	○ Other

Goal

Start Date	Due Date

What I want to achieve?

How I will achieve my goal?

What means most to me?

Focus on...

Action Plan

Date	Action Steps

Goal Planner

| ○ Physical Health | ○ Mental Health | ○ Soul/Spirit | ○ Socia |
| ○ Family | ○ Finance | ○ Career | ○ Other |

Goal

	Start Date	Due Date	

What do I want to achieve?

How will I achieve my goal?

What means the most to me?

Focus on...

Action Plan

Date	Action Steps

Goal Planner

○ Physical Health	○ Mental Health	○ Soul/Spirit	○ Social
○ Family	○ Finance	○ Career	○ Other

Goal

Start Date	Due Date

What I want to achieve?

How I will achieve my goal?

What means most to me?

Focus on...

Action Plan

Date	Action Steps

Goal Planner

○ Physical Health	○ Mental Health	○ Soul/Spirit	○ Social
○ Family	○ Finance	○ Career	○ Other

Goal

	Start Date	Due Date	

What do I want to achieve?

How will I achieve my goal?

What means the most to me?

Focus on...

Action Plan

Date	Action Steps

Goal Planner

| ○ | Physical Health | ○ | Mental Health | ○ | Soul/Spirit | ○ | Social |
| ○ | Family | ○ | Finance | ○ | Career | ○ | Other |

Goal

Start Date	Due Date

What I want to achieve?

How I will achieve my goal?

What means most to me?

Focus on...

Action Plan

Date	Action Steps

Goal Planner

○ Physical Health	○ Mental Health	○ Soul/Spirit	○	Socia
○ Family	○ Finance	○ Career	○	Other

Goal

Start Date	Due Date

What do I want to achieve?

_____
_____
_____
_____

How will I achieve my goal?

_____
_____
_____
_____

What means the most to me?

_____
_____
_____
_____

Focus on...

_____
_____
_____
_____

Action Plan

Date	Action Steps

Goal Planner

○	Physical Health	○	Mental Health	○	Soul/Spirit	○	Social
○	Family	○	Finance	○	Career	○	Other

Goal

	Start Date	Due Date	

What I want to achieve?

How I will achieve my goal?

What means most to me?

Focus on...

Action Plan

Date	Action Steps

Goal Planner

| ○ | Physical Health | ○ | Mental Health | ○ | Soul/Spirit | ○ | Socia |
| ○ | Family | ○ | Finance | ○ | Career | ○ | Other |

Goal

| | Start Date | Due Date | |
| | | | |

What do I want to achieve?

How will I achieve my goal?

What means the most to me?

Focus on...

Action Plan

Date	Action Steps

Goal Planner

○ Physical Health	○ Mental Health	○ Soul/Spirit	○ Social
○ Family	○ Finance	○ Career	○ Other

Goal

	Start Date	Due Date	

What I want to achieve?

How I will achieve my goal?

What means most to me?

Focus on...

Action Plan

Date	Action Steps

Goal Planner

| ○ Physical Health | ○ Mental Health | ○ Soul/Spirit | ○ Socia |
| ○ Family | ○ Finance | ○ Career | ○ Othe |

Goal	

	Start Date	Due Date	

What do I want to achieve?

How will I achieve my goal?

What means the most to me?

Focus on...

Action Plan

Date	Action Steps

Goal Planner

○	Physical Health	○	Mental Health	○	Soul/Spirit	○	Social
○	Family	○	Finance	○	Career	○	Other

Goal

	Start Date	Due Date	

What I want to achieve?

How I will achieve my goal?

What means most to me?

Focus on...

Action Plan

Date	Action Steps

Goal Planner

| ○ Physical Health | ○ Mental Health | ○ Soul/Spirit | ○ Socia |
| ○ Family | ○ Finance | ○ Career | ○ Othe |

Goal

| | Start Date | Due Date | |
| | | | |

What do I want to achieve?

How will I achieve my goal?

What means the most to me?

Focus on...

Action Plan

Date	Action Steps

Goal Planner

| ○ | Physical Health | ○ | Mental Health | ○ | Soul/Spirit | ○ | Social |
| ○ | Family | ○ | Finance | ○ | Career | ○ | Other |

Goal

	Start Date	Due Date	

What I want to achieve?

How I will achieve my goal?

What means most to me?

Focus on...

Action Plan

Date	Action Steps

Goal Planner

| ○ Physical Health | ○ Mental Health | ○ Soul/Spirit | ○ Socia |
| ○ Family | ○ Finance | ○ Career | ○ Othe |

Goal

| | Start Date | Due Date | |
| | | | |

What do I want to achieve?

How will I achieve my goal?

What means the most to me?

Focus on...

Action Plan

Date	Action Steps

Goal Planner

⭕ Physical Health	⭕ Mental Health	⭕ Soul/Spirit	⭕ Social
⭕ Family	⭕ Finance	⭕ Career	⭕ Other

Goal

Start Date	Due Date

What I want to achieve?

How I will achieve my goal?

What means most to me?

Focus on...

Action Plan

Date	Action Steps

Goal Planner

| ○ Physical Health | ○ Mental Health | ○ Soul/Spirit | ○ Socia |
| ○ Family | ○ Finance | ○ Career | ○ Other |

Goal

	Start Date	Due Date	

What do I want to achieve?

How will I achieve my goal?

What means the most to me?

Focus on...

Action Plan

Date	Action Steps

Goal Planner

○ Physical Health ○ Mental Health ○ Soul/Spirit ○ Social
○ Family ○ Finance ○ Career ○ Other

Goal

Start Date	Due Date

What I want to achieve?

How I will achieve my goal?

What means most to me?

Focus on...

Action Plan

Date	Action Steps

Goal Planner

| ○ Physical Health | ○ Mental Health | ○ Soul/Spirit | ○ Socia |
| ○ Family | ○ Finance | ○ Career | ○ Other |

Goal

| | Start Date | Due Date | |
| | | | |

What do I want to achieve?

How will I achieve my goal?

What means the most to me?

Focus on...

Action Plan

Date	Action Steps

Goal Planner

| ◯ Physical Health | ◯ Mental Health | ◯ Soul/Spirit | ◯ Social |
| ◯ Family | ◯ Finance | ◯ Career | ◯ Other |

Goal

| | Start Date | Due Date | |
| | | | |

What I want to achieve?

How I will achieve my goal?

What means most to me?

Focus on...

Action Plan

Date	Action Steps

Goal Planner

| ○ Physical Health | ○ Mental Health | ○ Soul/Spirit | ○ Socia |
| ○ Family | ○ Finance | ○ Career | ○ Other |

Goal

	Start Date	Due Date	

What do I want to achieve?

How will I achieve my goal?

What means the most to me?

Focus on...

Action Plan

Date	Action Steps

Goal Planner

○ Physical Health	○ Mental Health	○ Soul/Spirit	○ Social
○ Family	○ Finance	○ Career	○ Other

Goal

Start Date	Due Date

What I want to achieve?

How I will achieve my goal?

What means most to me?

Focus on...

Action Plan

Date	Action Steps

Goal Planner

| ○ | Physical Health | ○ | Mental Health | ○ | Soul/Spirit | ○ | Social |
| ○ | Family | ○ | Finance | ○ | Career | ○ | Other |

Goal

	Start Date	Due Date	

What do I want to achieve?

How will I achieve my goal?

What means the most to me?

Focus on...

Action Plan

Date	Action Steps

Goal Planner

○ Physical Health	○ Mental Health	○ Soul/Spirit	○ Social
○ Family	○ Finance	○ Career	○ Other

Goal

Start Date	Due Date

What I want to achieve?

How I will achieve my goal?

What means most to me?

Focus on...

Action Plan

Date	Action Steps

Goal Planner

| ○ Physical Health | ○ Mental Health | ○ Soul/Spirit | ○ Socia |
| ○ Family | ○ Finance | ○ Career | ○ Othe |

Goal

	Start Date	Due Date	

What do I want to achieve?

How will I achieve my goal?

What means the most to me?

Focus on...

Action Plan

Date	Action Steps

Goal Planner

○	Physical Health	○	Mental Health	○	Soul/Spirit	○	Social
○	Family	○	Finance	○	Career	○	Other

Goal

Start Date	Due Date

What I want to achieve?

How I will achieve my goal?

What means most to me?

Focus on...

Action Plan

Date	Action Steps

Goal Planner

| ○ Physical Health | ○ Mental Health | ○ Soul/Spirit | ○ Socia |
| ○ Family | ○ Finance | ○ Career | ○ Othe |

Goal

	Start Date	Due Date	

What do I want to achieve?

How will I achieve my goal?

What means the most to me?

Focus on...

Action Plan

Date	Action Steps

Goal Planner

○ Physical Health	○ Mental Health	○ Soul/Spirit	○ Social
○ Family	○ Finance	○ Career	○ Other

Goal

Start Date	Due Date

What I want to achieve?

How I will achieve my goal?

What means most to me?

Focus on...

Action Plan

Date	Action Steps

Goal Planner

| ○ Physical Health | ○ Mental Health | ○ Soul/Spirit | ○ Socia |
| ○ Family | ○ Finance | ○ Career | ○ Other |

Goal

| | Start Date | Due Date | |
| | | | |

What do I want to achieve?

How will I achieve my goal?

What means the most to me?

Focus on...

Action Plan

Date	Action Steps

Habit Tracker

	Jan	Feb	Mar	Apr	May	Jun	Jul	Aug	Sep	Oct	Nov	Dec

Goal Planner

Date	Highlights	Date	Highlights

Goal Planner

Date	Highlights	Date	Highlights

Goal Planner

Date	Highlights	Date	Highlights

Goal Planner

Date	Highlights	Date	Highlights

New Year Reflection

Favorite Moments	Family Accomplishment

Relationship Accomplishment	Health Accomplishment

New Year Reflection

Career Accomplishment	Finance Accomplishment

Notes

Printed in Great Britain
by Amazon